BACH, J. S.

CONCERTO

in F minor

FOR PIANO AND ORCHESTRA

(EDWIN FISCHER)

TWO-PIANO SCORE

INTERNATIONAL MUSIC COMPANY
New York City

BACH, J. S.
(Johann Sebastian)

CONCERTO

in F minor

FOR PIANO AND ORCHESTRA

(EDWIN FISCHER)

TWO-PIANO SCORE

No. 545

INTERNATIONAL MUSIC COMPANY

511 FIFTH AVENUE   **NEW YORK CITY**

CONCERTO

J. S. BACH
(1685-1750)

Allegro moderato

Piano Solo

Allegro moderato

**Piano II
(Orchestra)**

| signifies a breathing spell

545

Published by International Music Company, New York City

•) To be executed :

10

545

12

545

1213

545